THE
PETER PATTER
BOOK

THE KING HAD A PLATTER OF BRISKET AND BATTER

THE
PETER PATTER
BOOK

RHYMES
for
CHILDREN

RHYMES BY
LEROY F. JACKSON

ILLUSTRATIONS BY
BLANCHE FISHER WRIGHT

BARNES & NOBLE
NEW YORK

To
ANDREW, PUDGE, AND BOBBY
My first appreciative audience

ISBN-13: 978-0-7607-9296-4
ISBN-10: 0-7607-9296-8

Printed and bound in China

1 3 5 7 9 10 8 6 4 2

A LIST OF THE RHYMES

PETER PATTER *told them to me,*
All the little rhymes,
Whispered them among the bushes
Half a hundred times.

Peter lives upon a mountain
Pretty near the sun,
Knows the bears and birds and rabbits
Nearly every one;
Has a home among the alders,
Bed of cedar bark,
Walks alone beneath the pine trees
Even when it's dark.

Squirrels tell him everything
That happens in the trees,
Cricket in the gander-grass
Sings of all he sees;
Rhymes from bats and butterflies,
Crabs and waterfowl;
But the best of all he gets
From his Uncle Owl.

Sometimes when its day-time,
But mostly in the night,
They sit beneath an oak tree
And hug each other tight,
And tell their rhymes and riddles
Where the catty creatures prowl —
Funny little Peter Patter
And his Uncle Owl.

JINGLE, JINGLE, JACK, A COPPER DOWN A CRACK

THE
PETER PATTER BOOK

A COPPER DOWN A CRACK

Jingle, jingle, Jack,
A copper down a crack.
Twenty men and all their wives,
With sticks and picks and pocket
    knives,
Digging for their very lives
To get the copper back.

I'M MUCH TOO BIG FOR A FAIRY

I'm much too big for a fairy,
And much too small for a man,
But this is true:
Whatever I do,
I do it the best I can.

A MATTER OF TASTE

"Thank you, dear," said the big
    black ant,
"I'd like to go home with you now,
    but I can't.
I have to hurry and milk my cows—
The aphid herds on the aster
    boughs."
And the ladybug said: "No doubt
    it's fine,
This milk you get from your
    curious kine,
But you know quite well it's my
    belief
Your cows are best when turned
    to beef."

Sweet milk from a nanny-goat in a
    blue cup—
Drink it, it's good for you, sonny,
'Twill fill you, expand you, and
    help you grow up,
And make a real man of you,
    sonny.

HIPPITY HOP TO BED

O it's hippity hop to bed!
I'd rather sit up instead.
But when father says "must,"
There's nothing but just
Go hippity hop to bed.

THE BLUE SONG

Hot mush and molasses all in a
    blue bowl—
Eat it, it's good for you, sonny.
'Twill make you grow tall as a
    telephone pole—

Eat it, it's good for you, sonny.
Fresh fish and potatoes all on a
    blue plate—
Eat it up smart now, my sonny.
'Twill make you as jolly and fat as
    Aunt Kate—
Eat it up quick now, my sonny.

BOOTS, BOOTS, BOOTS

Buster's got a popper gun,
A reg'lar one that shoots,
And Teddy's got an engine
With a whistler that toots.
But I've got something finer yet —
A pair of rubber boots.
Oh, it's boots, boots, boots,
A pair of rubber boots!
I could walk from here to China
In a pair of rubber boots.

THE ANIMAL SHOW

Father and mother and Bobbie
   will go
To see all the sights at the animal
   show.
Where lions and bears
Sit on dining room chairs,
Where a camel is able
To stand on a table,
Where monkeys and seals
All travel on wheels,
And a Zulu baboon
Rides a baby balloon.
The sooner you're ready, the sooner
   we'll go.
Aboard, all aboard, for the Animal
   Show!

OUR LITTLE PAT

Our little Pat
Was chasing the cat
And kicking the kittens about.
When mother said "Quit!"
He ran off to sit
On the top of the woodpile and
   pout;
But a sly little grin
Soon slid down his chin
And let all the sulkiness out.

TOMMY TRIMBLE

Billy be nimble,
Hurry and see
Old Tommy Trimble
Climbing a tree.
He claws with his fingers
And digs with his toes.
The longer he lingers
The slower he goes.

THE ANIMAL SHOW

AWAY TO THE RIVER

Away to the river, away to the wood,
While the grasses are green and the berries are
    good!
Where the locusts are scraping their fiddles
    and bows,
And the bees keep a-coming wherever one goes.

Oh, it's off to the river and off to the hills,
To the land of the bloodroot and wild daffodils,
With a buttercup blossom to color my chin,
And a basket of burs to put sandberries in.

I Went To Town
On Monday

I went to town on Monday
To buy myself a coat,
But on the way I met a man
Who traveled with a caravan,
And bought a billy-goat.

I went to town on Tuesday
And bought a fancy vest.
I kept the pretty buckle-straps,
Buttonholes and pocketflaps,
And threw away the rest.

I went to town on Thursday
To buy a loaf of bread,
But when I got there, goodness
        sakes!
The town was full of rattle-
        snakes —
The bakers all were dead.

I went to town on Saturday
To get myself a wife,
But when I saw the lady fair
I gnashed my teeth and pulled my
        hair
And scampered for my life.

THE ARMY OF THE QUEEN

O the Army of the Queen,
The Army of the Queen,
Some are dressed in turkey-red
And some are dressed in green;
A colonel and a captain,
A corporal in between,
Their guns are filled with powder
And their swords are bright and
    keen;
So toot your little trumpet
For the Army of the Queen.

IF I WERE RICHER

If I were richer
I'd buy a pitcher
With scenery on it.
'Jolica ware—
Storks here and there,
And a funny affair
With ladies on it.

In half a minute
I'd mix up in it
A wonderful drink—
Peppermint, ice,
Lemons and spice—
Taste, pretty nice,
What do you think?

ROMULUS

Romulus, Romulus,
Father of Rome,
Ran off with a wolf
And he wouldn't come home.
When he grew up
He founded a city
With an eagle, a bear,
And a tortoise-shell kitty.

TOOT YOUR LITTLE TRUMPET FOR THE ARMY OF THE QUEEN

WHERE ARE YOU GOING?

Where are you going, sister Kate?
I'm going to swing on the garden
    gate,
And watch the fairy gypsies dance
Their tim-tam-tum on the
    cabbage-plants —
The great big one with the purple
    nose,
And the tiny tad with the pinky
    toes.

Where are you going, brother Ben?
I'm going to build a tiger-pen.
I'll get iron and steel and 'lectric
    wire
And build it a hundred feet or
    higher,
And put ten tigers in it too,
And a big wildcat, and — mebbe —
    you.

Where are you going, mother mine?
I'm going to sit by the old
    grapevine,
And watch the gliding swallow
    bring
Clay for her nest from the meadow
    spring—
Clay and straw and a bit of thread
To weave it into a baby's bed.

Where are you going, grandma dear?
I'm going, love, where the skies are
    clear,
And the light winds lift the poppy
    flowers
And gather clouds for the summer
    showers,
Where the old folks and the
    children play
On the warm hillside through the
    livelong day.

CHRISTOPHER CRUMP

Christopher Crump,
All in a lump,
Sits like a toad on the top of a
    stump.
He stretches and sighs,
And blinks with his eyes,
Bats at the beetles and fights off
the flies.

CONSOLATION

A dime and a dollar
Took me by the collar
And whispered this word in my ear:

"We must leave you tomorrow,
But prithee don't sorrow,
We'll come back to see you next year."

TICK, TOCK

Tick, tock! Tick, tock!
Forty 'leven by the clock.
Tick, tock! Tick, tock!
Put your ear to Grandpa's ticker,
Like a pancake, only thicker.
Tick, tock! Tick, tock!
Catch a squirrel in half a minute,
Grab a sack and stick him in it.
Tick, tock! Tick, tock!
Mister Bunny feeds on honey,
Tea, and taters —ain't it funny?
Tick, tock! Tick, tock!
When he goes to bed at night,
Shoves his slippers out of sight;
That is why Old Fox, the sinner,
Had to go without his dinner.
Tick, tock! Tick, tock!
So says Grandpa's clock.

SIX LITTLE SALMON

I sing a funny song from away out
    west,
Of six little salmon with their hats on;
How they all left home—but I
    forget the rest—
The six little salmon with their
    hats on.

PINKY, PINKY, PANG

A tortoise sat on a slippery limb
And played his pinky pang
For a dog-fish friend that called
    on him,
And this is what he sang:
"Oh, the skies are blue,
And I wait for you
To come where the willows hang,
And dance all night
By the white moonlight
To my pinky, pinky, pang!"

TICK, TOCK! TICK, TOCK! FORTY 'LEVEN BY THE CLOCK

I'VE GOT A NEW BOOK

I've got a new book from my Grandfather Hyde.

It's skin on the cover and paper inside,

And reads about Arabs and horses and slaves,

And tells how the Caliph of Bagdad behaves.

I'd not take a goat and a dollar beside

For the book that I got from my Grandfather Hyde.

Did You Ever Play Tag With A Tiger?

Did you ever play tag with a tiger,
Or ever play boo with a bear;
Did you ever put rats in the
    rain-barrel
To give poor old Granny a scare?

It's fun to play tag with a tiger,
It's fun for the bear to say "boo,"
But if rats are found in the
    rain-barrel
Old Granny will put you in too.

Tommy, My Son

"Tommy, my son," said the old
    tabby cat,
"Go catch us some mice, and be
    sure that they're fat.
There's one family lives in the
    carpenter's barn;
They've made them a nest of the
    old lady's yarn.
But the carpenter has a young cat
    of his own
That is healthy and proud and
    almost full grown,

And consider it, son, an eternal
    disgrace
To come home at night with a
    scratch on your face."

Oh, Said The Worm

"Oh," said the worm,
"I'm awfully tired of sitting in the
    trees;
I want to be a butterfly
And chase the bumblebees."

THE WIND

The wind came a-whooping down
    Cranberry Hill
And stole an umbrella from
    Mother Medill.

It picked up a paper on Patterson's
    place
And carried it clean to the Rockaby
    Race.

And what was more shocking and
    awful than that,
It blew the new feather off
    grandmother's hat.

BUZZY BROWN

Buzzy Brown came home
    from town
As crazy as a loon,
He wore a purple overcoat
And sang a Sunday tune.

Buzzy Brown came home from
    town
As proud as he could be,
He found three doughnuts and
    a bun
A-growing on a tree.

THE HOBO BAND

The roads are good and the
    weather's grand,
So I'm off to play in the Hobo
    Band;
With a gaspipe flute and a cowhide
    drum
I'm going to make the music come.
With a toot, toot, toot, and a dum,
    dum, dum,
Just hear me make the music come!

THE WIND CAME A-WHOOPING DOWN CRANBERRY HILL

DOCTOR DRAKE

On a hummock by the lake
Stands the home of Doctor Drake,
Poor old doctor, how he works!
Week by week he never shirks—

Pulling teeth for guinea-fowl,
Soothing puppies when they howl,
Whittling out a hickory peg
For a gander's broken leg

Giving medicine away
About a hundred times a day,
Linseed oil and elder-bark
To a croaking meadowlark,

Nasty, bitter yarrow-tea
To a tipsy bumble-bee,
A poultice made of
    plantain leaves
To cure a rabbit with
    the heaves.

Fever, colic, cramp, or stitch,
Kitten-croup or beaver's-itch,
Any kind of pain or ache
Is cured by dear, old Doctor Drake.

HOOTEM, TOOTEM, CLEAR THE TRACK

Hootem, tootem, clear the track!
I caught a coon on Kamiak!
Colonel Clapp and Uncle Rome
Have hired a hack to bring him
    home.

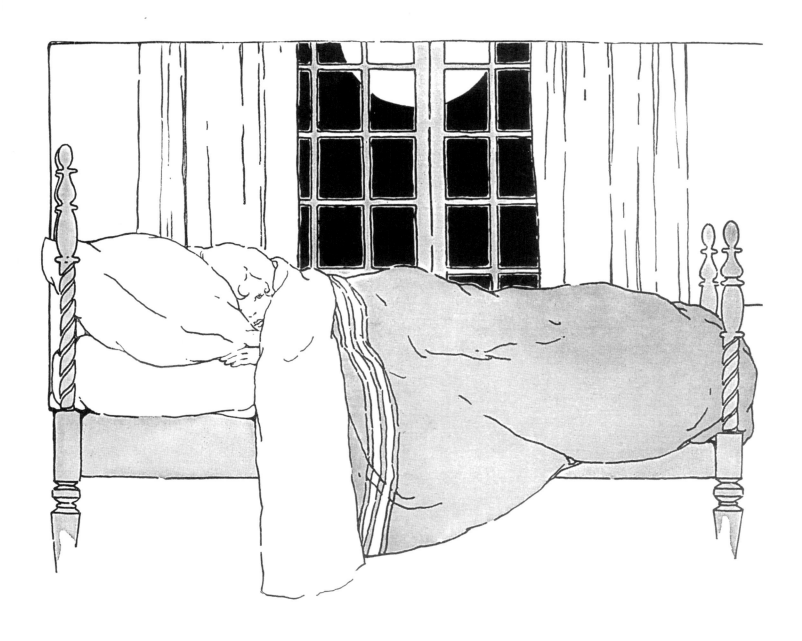

A CANDLE, A CANDLE

A candle, a candle
To light me to bed;
A pillow, a pillow
To tuck up my head.
The moon is as sleepy as sleepy
    can be,
The stars are all pointing their
    fingers at me,

And Missus Hop-Robin, way up in
    her nest,
Is rocking her tired little babies to
    rest.
So give me a blanket
To tuck up my toes,
And a little soft pillow
To snuggle my nose.

BAXTER

Baxter had a billy-goat
Wall-eyed and double jointed.
He took him to the barber shop
And had his head anointed.

LODDY, GIN, AND ELLA ZANDER

Loddy, Gin, and Ella Zander
Rode to market on a gander;
Bought a crane for half a dollar;
Loddy led him by the collar.

Mister Crane said: "Hi there,
    master,
Can't you make your legs work
    faster?

We can't poke along this way."
Then he slowly flew away.
Loddy held him fast, you bet,
And he hasn't come home yet.

AS I WAS GOING DOWN THE HILL

As I was going down the hill
In front of Missus Knapp's
I saw the little Knapperines
All in their winter wraps—
Purple mitts and mufflers
And knitted jersey caps.

As I was coming back again
In front of Missus Knapp's
I saw that awful lady
Give about a dozen slaps
To every little Knapperine—
I thought it was, perhaps,
Because they gathered stickers
In their knitted jersey caps.

HARRY HOOKER

Harry Hooker had a book
And couldn't find a teacher.
But still he managed very well,
He climbed a box and rang a bell
And turned into a preacher.

GOING DOWN THE HILL IN FRONT OF MISSUS KNAPP'S

A Little Boy Ran To The End Of The Sky

A little boy ran to the end of the sky
With a rag and a pole and a gooseberry pie.
He cried: "Three cheers for the Fourth of July!"
With a rag and a pole and a gooseberry pie.

He saw three little donkeys at play,
He tickled their noses to make them bray,
And he didn't come back until Christmas Day—
With a rag and a pole and a gooseberry pie.

Twenty Little Snowflakes

Twenty little snowflakes climbing
    up a wire.
"Now, listen," said their mother,
    "don't you climb up any
    higher.
The sun will surely catch you,
    and scorch you with his fire."
But the naughty little snowflakes
    didn't mind a word she said,
Each tried to clamber faster than
    his fellow just ahead;
They thought that they'd be
    back in time enough to go
    to bed.
But they found out that their
    mother wasn't quite the
    dunce they thought her,
The sun bobbed up—remember
    this, my little son and
    daughter—
And turned those twenty
    snowflakes into twenty drops
    of water.

Slippery Slim

Slippery Slim, a garter snake,
Leaned against a garden rake
And smiled a sentimental smile
At Tilly Toad, on the gravel pile,
Till that bashful miss was forced
    to hop
And hide her face in a carrot-top.

DUCKLE, DAISY

Duckle, duckle, daisy,
Martha must be crazy,
She went and made a Christmas cake
Of olive oil and gluten-flake,
And set it in the sink to bake,
Duckle, duckle, daisy.

TIPSY TOM

Tipsy Tom, the naughty fellow,
Dressed his wife in pink and
    yellow,
Set her in an apple tree,
And said: "Now catch a
    bumblebee."

GRANDMOTHER GRUNDY

O Grandmother Grundy,
Now what would you say
If the katydids carried
Your glasses away—

Carried them off
To the top of the sky
And used them to watch
The eclipses go by?

DUCKLE, DUCKLE, DAISY

So they got their plates and knives,
Their children and their wives,
And gobbled up the beetle on the
    broomstraw.

MULE THOUGHTS

A silly little mule
Sat on a milking stool
And tried to write a letter to his
    father.
But he couldn't find the ink,
So he said: "I rather think
This writing letters home is too
    much bother."

A BEETLE ON A BROOMSTRAW

A robin and a wren, as they walked
    along one night,
Saw a big brown beetle on a
    broomstraw.
Said the robin to the wren: "What
    a pretty, pretty sight —
That big brown beetle on a
    broomstraw!"

HIPPERTY, CLICKERTY, CLACKERTY, BANG

Hipperty, clickerty, clackerty, bang,
Get in a corner as fast as you can!
The sideboard is tipsy, the table is
    mad,
The chairs have lost all the sense
    that they had.
So hipperty, clickerty, clackerty,
    bang,
Get in a corner as fast as you can!

THE ROBIN AND THE SQUIRREL

Said the Robin to the Squirrel,
"How d' you do?"
Said the Squirrel to the Robin,
"How are you?"
"Oh, I've got some cherry pies,
And a half a dozen flies,
And a kettle full of beetles on
    to stew."

Said the Squirrel to the Robin,
"How d' you do?"
Said the Robin to the Squirrel,
"How are you?"
"I've a nest that's nice and neat,
And a wife that can't be beat,
And I'm every bit as happy now
    as you."

CONFIDENCE

CONFIDENCE

There's a corner, way down by the
    river,
Shut in by a big cedar log,
Where there's all kinds of creepers
    and crawlers,
Some whoppers—as big as a frog.

If you can keep quiet about it,
And not tell either Pinkey or
    Dan,
I'm not saying but mebbe I'll give
    you
Four or five to take home in a can.

BING, BANG, BING

A little boy bought him a great big
    gun—
Bing, Bang, Bing!
He shot three hummingbirds on
    the run,
And an elephant on the wing.

He drove all the snakes from the
    county roads,
And the beetles from the trees;
He killed all the bats and the warty
    toads,
And everything else like these.

So here's to the boy with the great
    big gun!
Sing, my laddies, sing!
Who shot three hummingbirds on
    the run,
And an elephant on the wing.

BEELA BY THE SEA

Catch a floater, catch an eel,
Catch a lazy whale,
Catch an oyster by the heel
And put him in a pail.

There's lots of work for Uncle Ike,
Fatty Ford and me
All day long and half the night
At Beela by the sea.

BUTTERFLY

Butterfly, butterfly,
Sit on my chin,
Your wings are like tinsel,
So yellow and thin.

Butterfly, butterfly,
Give me a kiss;
If you give me a dozen
There's nothing amiss.

Butterfly, butterfly,
Off to the flowers —
Wee, soulless sprite
Of the long summer hours.

BLUE FLAMES AND RED FLAMES

Blue flames and red flames
In a world all dark;
Blue flames and red flames,
And a tiny spark
Hurrying to heaven, lest it should
    be late;
Lest the cautious seraphim close
    the shining gate,
And leave the little wanderer
    forevermore to fly
Like an orphan angel through the
    endless sky.

TIMOTHY GRADY

Poor little Timothy Grady
Screwed up his face at a lady,
And, jiminy jack!
It wouldn't come back.
The louder he hollered
The tighter it grew,
His eyes are all red
And his lips are all blue.
Oh, mercy me, what in the
world will he do?
Poor little Timothy Grady!

CAPTAIN TICKLE AND HIS NICKEL

Captain Tickle had a nickel
In a paper sack,
He threw it in the river
And he couldn't get it back.
Captain Tickle spent his nickel
For a rubber ball,
And when he cut it open
There was nothing there at all.

HI! HI! WHO WILL BUY A WEE LITTLE CLOUD

A Race, A Race To Moscow

A race, a race to Moscow,
Before the close of day!
A race, a race to Moscow,
A long, long way!
First comes a butterfly a-riding
    on a frog,
Next comes a water rat a-floating
    on a log;
A caterpillar on the fence, a
    hopper in the hay—
Who'll get to Moscow before the
    close of day?

The Salesman

Hi! Hi! Who will buy
A wee little cloud for the pretty
    blue sky?
Some are purple, some are red,
And all are soft as a feather bed.
Hi! Little children, won't anyone
    buy
One little cloud for the pretty
    blue sky?

A Prince From Pepperville

A prince came down from
    Pepperville
In satin and in lace,
He wore a bonnet on his head
And whiskers on his face.

And when he came to Battleburg
This is what befell:
He gave the king and cabinet
A half a peanut shell.

KING KOKEM

King Kokem lay snoozing upon his brass bed—
Oh, play an old tune on your fiddle!
With shoes on his feet, and a crown on his head—
Oh, tune up your rusty old fiddle!
He dreamed of a land where the lions were tame,
Where they fried their lamb-chops on a griddle,

Where they called all the parrots
and monkeys by name —
Oh, play us a tune on your fiddle!
He dreamed of a sea filled with
raspberry pop,
With a cocoanut isle in the
middle,
Where the stones and the
boulders had icing on top —
Go strike up a tune on your
fiddle!

He dreamed of a sky where the
moonbeams all danced
While a comet was telling a riddle,
Where the stars and the planets
and sun-dogs all pranced
While the moon played his fiddle
de diddle.

OLD MISSUS SKINNER

Old Missus Skinner
Had dumplings for dinner
And sat on a very high stool;
When she cut thru the hide
There was nothing inside,
Which I'm sure was not often
the rule.

THE RUNAWAYS

A pipe and a spoon and a tenpenny
   nail
Stole a tin dishpan and went for
   a sail.
But the cook he grew curious,
Fussy, and furious;
Gathered his trappings, and went
    on their trail.
He found them that night in a
    pitiful plight,
And sent them all home on the ten
    o'clock mail.

NEEDLES AND PINS

Needles and pins, hooks and eyes!
I saw a doughnut in the skies.
Flipperjinks the circus clown
Climbed a tree and got it down.

PLENTY

There are plenty feathers on a hen
And prickers on a rose,
There is plenty roaring in a den
Of lions, goodness knows;

There are plenty fishes in the lake
And islands in the sea;
There are plenty raisins in this
    cake
For even you and me.

NEEDLES AND PINS, HOOKS AND EYES!

BILLY BUMPKINS

Heigho, Billy Bumpkins,
How d' you grow
    your pumpkins?
"At six o'clock I sows 'em,
At ten o'clock I hoes 'em,
An' jes before I goes to bed
I puts 'em in the pumpkin shed."

Tell us, Billy Bumpkins,
How d' you sell
    your pumpkins?
"I lends 'em to the ladies,
I gives 'em to the babies,
An' trades a hundred for a kiss
To any pretty little miss."

A FREE SHOW

Mister McCune
Can whistle a tune,

Old Uncle Strong
Can sing us a song,

Benjamin Biddle
Can play on the fiddle,

Captain O'Trigg
Can dance us a jig,

And I, if I'm able,
Will tell you a fable.

SIMPLE SAM

Said Simple Sam: "Does Christmas
    come
In April or December,
In winter, spring, or harvest time?
I really can't remember."

USEFUL KNOWLEDGE

Candy is sticky,
Sugar is sweet;
When cattle are killed
They are turned into meat.

Finches are yellow,
Ravens are black;
Puppies run off
And never come back.

Father is fat,
Mother is lean,
And Missus Maloney
Is half way between.

OLD MOLLY IS LOWING

Old Molly is lowing and lowing
'Way down in the old meadow lot.
I've given her water and clover,
And all of the apples I've got;

But she won't eat a thing that I
    give her,
And never drinks even a sup,
For they've taken her baby to
    market
And some one has eaten it up.
I'd just like to go to the city
And cut them all up into halves
And feed them to sharks and to
    lions —
Those people that eat little calves.

OH, MOTHER

Oh, Mother, Oh, Mother,
Come quickly and see,
The house and the farmyard
Have gone on a spree.

The pig's in the pantry,
The chickens are out,
The parrot is perched
On the tea kettle spout.

And mercy, Oh, mercy,
Oh, what shall I do?
A rat has run off
With my very best shoe.

POLLY AND PETER

Polly had some china cows
And Peter had a gun.
She turned the bossies out to
    browse,
And Peterkin, for fun,
Just peppered them with butter
    beans
And blew them all to smithereens.
Now what will pretty Polly do
For milk and cream and butter
    too?

OH MOTHER, OH MOTHER, COME QUICKLY AND SEE

PENSIVE PERCY

Percy when a little boy
Was quiet as a mouse,
He never set the barn afire
Nor battered down the house.

He used to sit for hours and hours
Just gazing at the moon,
And feeding little fishes
Sarsaparilla from a spoon.

THE HERO

My dad was a soldier and fought
    in the wars,
My grandfather fought on the sea,
And the tales of their daring and
    valor of course
Put the sand and the ginger in me.

I'm not scared of tigers or any
    wild beast,
I could fight with a lion all right,
I wouldn't be 'fraid of a bear in
    the least—
Excepting, perhaps, in the night.

But sister, she's skeery as skeery
    can be,
She's even afraid of the bark of
    a tree.

HIGH ON THE MANTEL

High on the mantel rose a
    moan—
It came from an idol carved in
    bone—
"Oh, it's so lonesome here alone,
With no one near to love me!"

A cautious smile came over
    the face
Of a pensive maid on a Grecian
    vase.
"Are you sure" she said, with
    charming grace,
"There's no one near to love you?"

UNDER THE WILLOW

Put down your pillow under the
    willow,
Hang up your hat in the sun,
And lie down to snooze as long as
    you choose,
For the plowing and sowing are
    done.

Pick up your pillow from under
    the willow,
And clamber out into the sun.
Get a fork and a rake for goodness'
    sake,
For the harvest time has begun.

TRANSFORMATION

JOLLY JINKS

Jolly Jinks, the sailor man,
Went to sea in an oyster can.
But he found the water wet,
Fishes got into his net,
So he pulled his boat to shore
And vowed he'd sail the seas
no more.

TRANSFORMATION

Auntie Ellen found her poodle —
Mercy! Goodness sake! —
Playing with the mully-wumps
Down along the lake.

And when she called him tenderly
He didn't want to come;
It took her over half an hour
To get the rascal home.

She washed him well with
    shaving-soap,
Pumice stone and lye,
She showered him and she scoured
    him
And she hung him up to dry.

And now he sits there quite
    serene,
The sweetest poodle ever seen.

THE THIEVES

Tibbitts and Bibbitts and Solomon
    Sly
Ran off one day with a cucumber
    pie.
Tibbitts was tossed by a
    Kensington cow,
Bibbitts was hanged on a
    brambleweed bough,
And poor little Solomon — what
    do you think?
Was drowned one dark night in a
    bottle of ink.

CROWN THE KING WITH CARROT TOPS

Crown the king with carrot tops,
Dress him in sateen,
Give him lots of licorice drops,
With suckers in between.

For he's a king with lots of power
And awful, awful fierce,
He kills a pirate every hour
And washes in his tears.

He rides a charger ten feet high,
A dashing, dappled gray;
Has ginger pop and lemon pie
For breakfast every day.

So get a royal canopy,
The finest ever seen,
And whiskers for his majesty,
And tresses for the queen.

THE CANADA GOOSE

A Canada goose
On the South Palouse
Is singing her summer song.
Her words are wise,
And she greets the skies
With a voice like a steamer gong:
"If you harbor your wealth
And keep your health,
You'll always be rich and strong."

SOMEBODY

Somebody give me a peanut,
Somebody give me a pear;
I want to go down to the circus
And feed all the animals there.

I met the goat
That ate his coat
Upon the road to Terre Haute.

At last all worn
And quite forlorn
I chased him up the Matterhorn.

TWENTY THIEVES
FROM ALBION

Twenty thieves from Albion,
All with butcher knives,
Coming on the dead run,
Fighting for their lives.

See the man from our town.
In a fancy vest,
Knocking all the big ones down,
Chasing all the rest.

THE THIEF CHASE

Bricks and bones!
Sticks and stones!
I chased a thief through twenty
    zones.

I found his hat
On Ararat,
And hurried on as quick as scat.

In a day or two
I found his shoe
Where he had sailed for
    Timbuktu.

TO GARRY ON THE TOOT-TOOT

Oh, I want to go to Garry
On the toot-toot, toot-toot,
You and I together
On the toot-toot, toot-toot.
Go run and ask your mother
For some kind of cake or other,
And a bit of cotton wadding
For your ball-suit.
Get your bobber and a bat,
And be back as quick as scat,
For we've got to go to Garry
On the toot-toot.

DOUBBLEDOON

Bobbin rode a rocking-horse
'Way down to Doubbledoon,
He told his little sister
He'd be back that afternoon.
But maybe after all she didn't
Understand him right,
For he wasn't back again
Till the middle of the night.

And what did little Bobbin see
'Way down at Doubbledoon?
He saw a crazy Arab
Throwing bubbles at the moon,
A monkey making faces
And a rabbit in a rage,
A parrot shouting "Murder!"
From the ceiling of his cage.

At last a yellow jumping-jack,
A camel, and a coon,
Chased poor little Bobbin
All the way from Doubbledoon.

BOBBIN RODE A ROCKING-HORSE TO DOUBBLEDOON

THE THUNDER BABY

Have you heard of the Thunder
    Baby
Way up in the big blue sky?
You've seen his cradle, maybe,
And maybe you've heard him cry.

Most of the time he's sleeping,
Rolled up in a big white
    cloud,
But when he's awake
    and hungry
He bellows awfully loud.

And when he's crying, sometimes
You can hear his teardrops fall
With a patter, patter, patter,
Against the garden wall.

But when he's madder'n mischief,
He rolls, and growls, and spits,
And kicks the clouds all forty
    ways,
And gives the weather fits.

Then tears come down in
    bucketfuls,
And children dance for joy,
Till the sun comes out and soundly
    spanks
Her Thunder Baby Boy.

RED LEMONADE AND A CIRCUS PARADE

Red Lemonade
And a circus parade!
Toop-tittle, toop-tittle, tum-tum-tum!
An African horse,
And a camel, of course,
Toop-tittle, toop-tittle, tum-tum-tum!
It's hippity hopper and hippity ho,
We're off for a day at the elephant show,
With a toop-tittle, toop-tittle, tum-tum-tum!

SNOWFLAKES

The snowflakes are falling by ones
   and by twos;
There's snow on my jacket, and
   snow on my shoes;
There's snow on the bushes, and
   snow on the trees —
It's snowing on everything now,
   if you please.

CELLA REE AND TOMMY TO

Two funny friends that you all know
Are Cella Ree and Tommy To.
About as queer as friends can be,
Are Tommy To and Cella Ree.
For hours they sit there grim and
   stable
Side by side upon the table.
Tom is red and Cella pale,
His blushes are of no avail;
She sits, in spite of his endeavor,
As firm and undisturbed as ever,
A funny pair, you must agree,
This Tommy To and Cella Ree.

DICKIE, DICKIE DEXTER

Dickie, Dickie Dexter
Had a wife and vexed her.
She put him in a rabbit cage
And fed him peppermint and
   sage —
Dickie, Dickie Dexter.

THE SNOWFLAKES ARE FALLING BY ONES AND BY TWOS

HINKY, PINKY, PEARLY EARL

Hinky, pinky, pearly earl,
Twenty nobles and a churl;
Some are fat and some are lean,
One in red and one in green—
Prior, priest, and pearly earl,
Twenty nobles and a churl.

A TOE RHYME

Tassle is a captain,
Tinsel is a mayor,
Tony is a baker-boy
With 'lasses in his hair,
Tipsy is a sailor,
With anchors on his chest,
And Tiny is the baby boy
Who bosses all the rest.

POLLY PICKLENOSE

"Polly, Polly, goodness gracious!
You just quit your making faces."
Polly laughed at what they said,
Cocked her nose and went
    to bed.

But the big black Bugoo heard,
And he came without a word;
Walked right in—you bet a
    nickel!
In his hand a great green pickle;

Stalked along with steady pace,
Stuck it right in Polly's face,
Pinned it fast, and there
    it grows—
Poor Polly
    Picklenose!

I'll have some men in soldier
    tents,
A pirate and his mate,
And wildcats all around the fence,
And mad dogs on the gate.

THE KING HAD A PLATTER

The King had a platter
Of brisket and batter,
The Prince had a Bellington bun,
The Queen had a rose
To put to her nose
    As soon as the dinner was done

RINKY-TATTLE

Rinky-tattle, rinky-tattle,
Rinky-tattle —who?
Little Tommy Taylor
Is a rinky-tattle too.

WHEN I'M AS RICH AS UNCLE CLAUS

When I'm as rich as Uncle Claus,
With whiskers on my chin,
I'm going to have a great big
    house
To put my people in.

I'll never let them wander out
Or ride with me to town;
They'll come a-running when
    I shout
And tremble when I frown.

DOCTOR MCSWATTLE FILLED UP A BOTTLE

DOCTOR McSWATTLE

Doctor McSwattle
Filled up a bottle
With vinegar, varnish, and rum.
And offered a swallow
To all who would follow
The call of his trumpet and drum.
It's good, I am told,
For a cough or a cold;
It's good for a pain in your thumb.

COLUMBUS

Columbus sailed over the ocean
    blue
To find the United States.
In three small ships he carried
    his crew,
And none of the three were mates.

He found a land in the western seas,
And Indians galore,
With jabbering parrots in the trees,
And sharks along the shore.

He filled his pockets with
    sparkling stones
And took to the mighty main,
With a couple of slaves, some nuts
    and cones
For the glorious king of Spain.

Now this is the tale Columbus
    told,
And most of the tale is true,
How he crossed the seas, a sailor
    bold,
In fourteen-ninety-two.

DIPPY-DIPPY-DAVY

Dippy-Dippy-Davy,
Half the Royal Navy
In the dampness and the dark
Was driving off a savage shark
To Dippy-Dippy-Davy.

PADDY WENT TO PENDLETON

Paddy went to Pendleton
With money in his pocket
And bought the pretty ladies each
A shining silver locket.

Paddy went to Bunnyville
On Sunday afternoon
And fed the little bunnies
Bread and gravy with a spoon.

But Paddy is a hero now,
A mighty hero too,
He saved poor Sally's kitten
From a pot of gummy glue.

ON THE ROAD TO TATTLETOWN

On the road to Tattletown
What is this I see?
A pig upon a pedestal,
A cabbage up a tree,
A rabbit cutting capers
With a twenty dollar bill—
Now if I don't get to Tattletown
Then no one ever will.

JIGGER-JAGGER

Jigger-jagger rag-a-tagger,
Going to the mill;
Jigger-jagger, rag-a-tagger,
Trotting down the hill,
A gunny-sack of Russian wheat,
A bushel-bag of Rye,
Jigger-jagger, lazy-bones,
We'll get there by and by.

As I Came Out Of Grundy Greet

As I came out of Grundy Greet
Four cats were marching down
    the street,

One was long and gray and thin
With lots of whiskers on his chin,

And one was round and sleek
    and fat
(He must have been a butcher's cat).

One was dapper, slight, and frail,
With bells and tassels on his tail,

And one had starey yellow eyes
Almost as big as pumpkin pies.

These four came marching down
    the street
As I came out of Grundy Greet.

Babies

Come to the land where the babies
    grow,
Like flowers in the green, green
    grass.

Tiny babes that swing and crow
Whenever the warm winds pass,

And laugh at their own bright eyes
    aglow
In a fairy looking-glass.

Come to the sea where the babies
    sail
In ships of shining pearl,
Borne to the west by a golden
    gale
Of sun-beams all awhirl;
And perhaps a baby brother will
    sail
To you, my little girl.

THROUGH FOG AND RAIN I RUN MY TRAIN

THE FREIGHTER

Through fog and rain
I run my train
Wherever the track is laid,
And over the road
I carry a load
Whenever the freight is paid.

A caddy of tea
For Genessee,
For Troy an empty crate,
A man in brown
For Uniontown
To help them celebrate.

NO ONE AT HOME

No one at home in the henhouse,
And no one at home in the barn,
Old Brindle has gone to the
    neighbor's
To borrow a skein of brown yarn,
To borrow yarn for the darning
Of socks for her wee spotted calf—
The little rollicking rascal
Has never enough by half.
And Speckle is down by the willow
Washing her chicks in the lake,
While old Daddy Cockle is lying
Abed with a bad toothache.

PATTERS AND TATTERS

Patters had a gallant band,
An army made of clay.
But Tatters took the garden hose
And washed them all away.

THE STOVE

A stove is a thing that gets awfully
    hot,
And fries up your meat, or
    whatever you've got.
It's made out of iron and hinges
    and screws,
And filled up with shakers, and
    dampers, and flues.
It's not very long and it's not very
    wide;
It's got black'ning on top and ashes
    inside.

MOON, O MOON IN THE EMPTY SKY

Moon, O Moon in the empty sky,
Why do you swing so low?
Pretty moon with the silver ring
And the long bright beams where the fairies cling,
Where do you always go?

I go to the land of the Siamese,
Ceylon and the Great Plateau,
Over the seas where Sinbad sailed,
Where Moses crossed and Pharaoh failed,—
There's where I always go.

THE CARROT AND THE RABBIT

A carrot in a garden
And a rabbit in the wood.
Said the rabbit, "Beg your pardon,
But you're surely meant for food;
Though you've started in to
    harden,
You may still be very good."

HIPPY-HI-HOPPY

Hippy-Hi-Hoppy, the big fat
    toad,
Greeted his friends at a turn of
    the road.

Said he to the snail:
"Here's a ring for your tail
If you'll go into town for my
    afternoon mail."

Said he to the rat:
"I have talked with the cat;
And she'll nab you so quick you
    won't know where you're at."

Said he to the lizard:
"I'm really no wizard,
But I'll show you a trick that will
    tickle your gizzard."

Said he to the lark:
"When it gets fairly dark
We'll chase the mosquitoes in
    Peek-a-Boo Park."

Said he to the owl:
"If it were not for your scowl
I'd like you as well as most any
    wild fowl."

Said he to the wren:
"You're tiny, but then
I'll marry you quick, if you'll only
    say when."

I'LL TREAT THE CLOWN

Up On The Garden Gate

Set me up on the garden gate
And put on my Sunday tie;
I want to be there
With a round-eyed stare
When the circus band goes by.

Give me a bag of suckerettes
And give me a piece of gum,
Then I'll get down
And treat the clown,
And give the monkey some.

'Most Any Chip

'Most any chip
Will do for a ship,
If only the cargo be
Golden sand
From the beautiful land
Of far-off Arcady.
For faith will waft
The tiny craft
O'er Fancy's shining sea.

A Moon Song

Who hung his hat on the moon?
The owl in his bubble balloon.
One bright summer night
He sailed out of sight,
And, hooting like Lucifer, hung
    in delight
His three-cornered hat on the
    moon.

WHAT MAKES YOU LAUGH?

"What makes you laugh, my little
    lass,
From morning until noon?"
"I saw a dappled donkey
Throwing kisses at the moon."

"What makes you cry, my little lass,
And get your eyes so red?"
"I saw a cruel gardener cut
A poor old cabbage head."

"What makes you run, my little lass?
You're almost out of breath."
"A pumpkin made a face at me,
And scared me half to Death."

TIMMY O'TOOLE

When Timmy O'Toole
Was going to school
He picked up a package of gum.
He treated the preacher
And Sunday-school teacher,
And gave a policeman some.

JERRY WAS A JOKER

Jerry was a joker.
He carried off the poker
And dressed it up from head to
    heel
In clover-tops and orange-peel
And fed it bones and barley meal.
Poor old Rusty Poker!

ALL ABOARD FOR BOMBAY

All aboard for Bombay,
All aboard for Rome!
Leave your little sisters
And your loving aunts at home.

Bring a bit of bailing wire,
A pocketful of nails,
And half a dozen wiener-wursts
For every man that sails.
Tell Terry Tagg, when you go by,
Be sure to bring his dog.
All aboard for Bombay
On a floating cedar log!

WATER

There's water in the rain barrel,
And water in the well,
There's lots of water in the pond
Where Hannah Hawkins fell.

There's water in the ocean,
And water in the skies,
And when a fellow blubbers
He gets water in his eyes.

But in the Barca desert
Where the hippodoodles play,
The water in the rivers
Just dries up and blows away.

BOATS

Hitch up your cattle
And drive to Seattle
To see all the boats come in, —
From Kibi and Kobi
And Panama Dobi
And some from the Islands of
    Myn.
They're bringing us rices
And cocoa and spices
And pineapples done up in tin,
And maybe Aunt Dinah
Will come back from China
If ever the boats get in.

PRETTY THINGS

Pretty poppies,
Pretty trees,
Pretty little lettuce-leaves,
Pretty pebbles,
Red and brown,
Pretty floating thistle-down.
Pretty baby,
Curly head,
Standing in a pansy-bed,
Pretty clouds
All white and curled—
O the great, big pretty world!

DID YOU EVER?

Did you ever go to the watering
    trough
And watch the sparrows drink?
Did you ever go to Potter's pond
And see the divers sink?
Did you ever steal to the barn at
    night
And watch the hoot-owls think?

PRETTY THINGS

But there came an awful clatter
From that elder tree,
When he served them on a platter
Hopper-hash and brick-dust
　　　batter
Trimmed with celery!

All the folks were hale and
　　　hearty,
Happy as could be;
And that little black-eyed smarty
Left out of his funny party
Only you and me.

THE PARTY

Billy Bluebird had a party
In an elder tree,
But the little black-eyed smarty
Didn't ask us to his party
Neither you nor me.

This is what they had for dinner,
For I peeked to see:
Apple seeds and beetle finner,
And for drink the little sinner
Gave them tansy tea.

WHAT'S THE USE?

"What's the use,"
Said the goose,
"To swim like a frog,
When you go just as far
If you float on a log?"

"Why should I,"
Said the fly,
"Suck an old apple-core,
When there's sugar and fruit
In the grocery store?"

"It's but right,"
Said the kite,
"That I follow the wind.
What's a fellow to do
If he hasn't a mind?"

"You'll allow,"
Said the cow,
"That I'm really no thief,
When I turn all the clover
I steal, into beef."

"Come again,"
Said the hen,
"On some other fine day.
Don't think 'cause I cackle
I always must lay."

TERRIBLE TIM

Haven't you heard of Terrible Tim?
Well, don't you get in the way of
    him.
He eats lions for breakfast
And leopards for lunch,
And gobbles them down
With one terrible crunch.
He could mix a whole city
All up in a mess,
He could drink up a sea
Or an ocean, I guess.
You'd better be watching for
    Terrible Tim,
And run when you first get your
    peepers on him.

RAG-MAN, RAG-MAN, TAGGY, TAGGY, RAG-MAN

The Rag-Man

"Rag-man, rag-man,
Taggy, taggy, rag-man,
Tell us what you've got there in
    your sack."

"Oh—it's full of rhymes and
    riddles,
Jingles, jokes, and hi-de-
    diddles—
This bundle that I carry on my
    back."

"O tell us, funny rag-man,
Grinny, skinny rag-man,
Where did you pick up your funny
    rhymes?"

"Some were dancing with
    corn-flowers,
Some were hiding in church-
    towers,
And sprinkled helter-skelter by
    the chimes."

"Rag-man, rag-man,
Nice old taggy rag-man,
Sing us just one jingle, tingle
    song."

"Why, my dears, I've got a plenty,
Sing you one? I'll sing you
    twenty—
I've been hoping you would ask me
    all along."

Whenever I Go Out To Walk

Whenever I go out to walk,
All the geese begin to gawk;
And when I start to wander back,
All the ducks begin to quack.

A BIG, FAT POTATO

A big, fat potato lay down on a clod
In the shade of some burdock and tall goldenrod,
And he dreamed he was king of the whole garden plot,
With a palace and throne, and a crown with a lot
Of jewels and diamonds and gold till it shone
Like the front of a show when the lights are turned on.

To be king and commander o'er all
the wide land.
But at last he woke up with an
awful surprise
And found a blind mole kicking
sand in his eyes.

A BUNDLE OF HAY

A bundle of hay
From Baffin's Bay,
A johnny-cake from Rome,
A man and a mule
From Ultima Thule
To carry the cargo home.

He had to be minded by all of the
plants;
When he whistled the radishes
knew they must dance;
When he tooted his horn the
cucumbers must sing
To a vegetable crowd gathered
round in a ring.
He made all the cabbages stand in
a row
While a sunflower instructed them
just how to grow;
The bright yellow pumpkins he
painted light blue;
Took the clothes off the scare-crow
and made him buy new.
He strutted and sputtered and
thought it was grand

SONNY

A sailor gave his sonny
Nearly half a pint of money
And sent him out to buy a ton of
    coal;
But he met a poor old miser
Who told him it were wiser
To bury all his money in a hole.

A sailor gave his sonny
Nearly half a pint of money
And told him he should buy a suit
    of clothes;
But he saw a pretty maiden
With all kinds of posies laden,
And he gave her all his money for
    a rose.

Then the sailor gave his sonny
Nearly half a pint of money
To buy a little garden and
    a house;
But he found him the next day,
In a shop on Yesler Way,
A-buying cheese and crackers for
    a mouse.

BARON BATTEROFF

The mighty baron, Batteroff,
Raised a whale in a watering
    trough.
When the whale grew large
    and fat
He ate the baron's brindle cat.
But pussy, once inside the whale,
Began to tickle with her tail.
This the monster could not stand,
And spewed her out upon dry land.
That night, when all was fine
    as silk
And she had supped her bread
    and milk,
She grinned and told old Batteroff
How she got the whale to cough.

HE GAVE HER ALL HIS MONEY FOR A ROSE

I'VE GOT A YELLOW PUPPY

I've got a yellow puppy,
And I've got a speckled hen,
I've got a lot of little
Spotted piggies in a pen.
I've got a gun that used to
    shoot,
Another one that squirts,

I've got some horehound candy
And a pair of woolen shirts.
I've got a little rubber ball
They use for playing golf,
And mamma thinks that's maybe
    why
I've got the whooping-cough.

DISCRETION

A man with a nickel,
A sword, and a sickle,
A pipe, and a paper of pins
Set out for the Niger
To capture a tiger—
And that's how my story begins.

When he saw the wide ocean,
He soon took a notion
'Twould be nicer to stay with his
    friends.
So he traded his hat
For a tortoise-shell cat—
And that's how the chronicle ends.

A BEETLE ONCE SAT ON A BARBERRY TWIG

A beetle once sat on a barberry
    twig,
And turned at the crank of a
    thingum-a-jig.
Needles for hornets, nippers for
    ants,
For the bumblebee baby a new pair
    of pants,
For the grizzled old gopher a hat
    and a wig,
The beetle ground out of his
    thingum-a-jig.

OLD FATHER MCNETHER

Old Father McNether
He sorts out the weather
And takes what he pleases,
    I'm told,
With a big turkey-feather
He mixes the weather,
And makes it blow hot and
    blow cold.

UPON THE IRISH SEA

Some one told Maria Ann,
Maria Ann told me,
That kittens ride in coffee cans
Upon the Irish Sea.

From quiet caves to rolling waves,
How jolly it must be
To travel in a coffee can
Upon the Irish Sea!

But when it snows and when it
    blows,
How would you like to be
A kitten in a coffee can
Upon the Irish Sea?

RAIN

The lightning split the sky in two
And set the clouds to leaking
Just as dear old Pastor Brown
Began his Sunday speaking.

He told about the awful rain
That fell in Noah's day,
And one by one the happy smiles
Began to fade away.

In half an hour the people all
Put on their rubber coats,
And when he finished everyone
Was out and building boats.

OLD FATHER MCNETHER

Well, they ate and ate and ate,
Gobbled at an awful rate
Till I'm sure they soon weighed
    more
Than double what they did before.
And then, it's awful, still it's true,
The floor gave way and they went
    thru.
Filled so full they couldn't fight,

JELLY JAKE AND
BUTTER BILL

Jelly Jake and Butter Bill
One dark night when all was still
Pattered down the long, dark stair,
And no one saw the guilty pair;
Pushed aside the pantry-door
And there found everything
    galore,—
Honey, raisins, orange-peel,
Cold chicken aplenty for a meal,
Gingerbread enough to fill
Two such boys as Jake and Bill.

Slowly they sank out of sight.
Father, Mother, Cousin Ann,
Cook and nurse and furnace man
Fished in forty-dozen ways
After them, for twenty days;
But not a soul has chanced to get
A glimpse or glimmer of them
     yet.
And I'm afraid we never will—
Poor Jelly Jake and Butter Bill.

CUT UP A CAPER

Cut up a caper,
You've got a paper
And I've got a widget of string.
You be the army
And let nothing harm me
For I am the captain and king.

A MAN CAME FROM MALDEN

A man came from Malden to buy
    a blue goose.
And what became of the gander?
He went and got tipsy on
    blackberry juice,
And that was the end of the
    gander.

WE'RE GOING TO HAVE A TREAT

EAT, EAT, EAT

Here come the sweet potatoes
And here's the Sunday meat,
I guess we must be ready now
To eat, eat, eat.

I'm going to have the nicey plate
And Daddy's leather seat,
And wear my patent-leather shoes
To eat, eat, eat.

My Daddy's talking all about
The war, and some old fleet,
I wonder if he never, never,
Never wants to eat.

We're going to have some
    apple-cake,
We're going to have a treat.
O hurry, hurry, Daddy,
Let us eat, eat, eat.

HETTY HUTTON

Hetty Hutton,
Here's a button,
Sew it on your dress.
Willie Waller,
Here's a dollar,
Maybe more or less.
Mister Shuster,
Here's a rooster,
Put him in a pen.
Mister Saxon,
Get an ax an'
Let him out again.

OLD FATHER ANNUM

Old Father Annum on New Year's
    Day
Picked up his bag of months and
    years,
Thrust in his hand in a careless
    way,
And pulled a wee fellow out by
    the ears.
"There you are," said he to the
    waiting crowd,
"He's as good as any I have in my
    pack.
I never can tell, but I hope to be
    proud
Of the little rascal when I come
    back."

PETER, POPPER

Peter, popper, dopper, Dan,
Catch a moonbeam if you can;
Climb a cedar ten feet high
And pick the planets from the
    sky.
You're a wonder, little man—
Peter, popper, dopper, Dan.

THE TIPPANY FLOWER

O what will you take for a tippany
    flower,
And what will you take for a
    pansy?
I'll take a smile for the tippany
    flower,
And a kiss for the pretty pansy.

OLD FATHER ANNUM

HERE COMES A CABBAGE

Here comes a cabbage with a bonnet on its head,
A pretty purple bonnet with a bow of blue and red;
And here comes a bottle with a collar 'round its neck,
A handsome linen collar, too, without a spot or speck;
Next comes a meat-saw, his job is biting beef,
And according to the cleaver he has gold in all his teeth;
And last of all there comes along, amid the ringing cheers,
A princely Indian corn-stalk with rings in both his ears.